This book belongs to:

_____

_____

C333242322

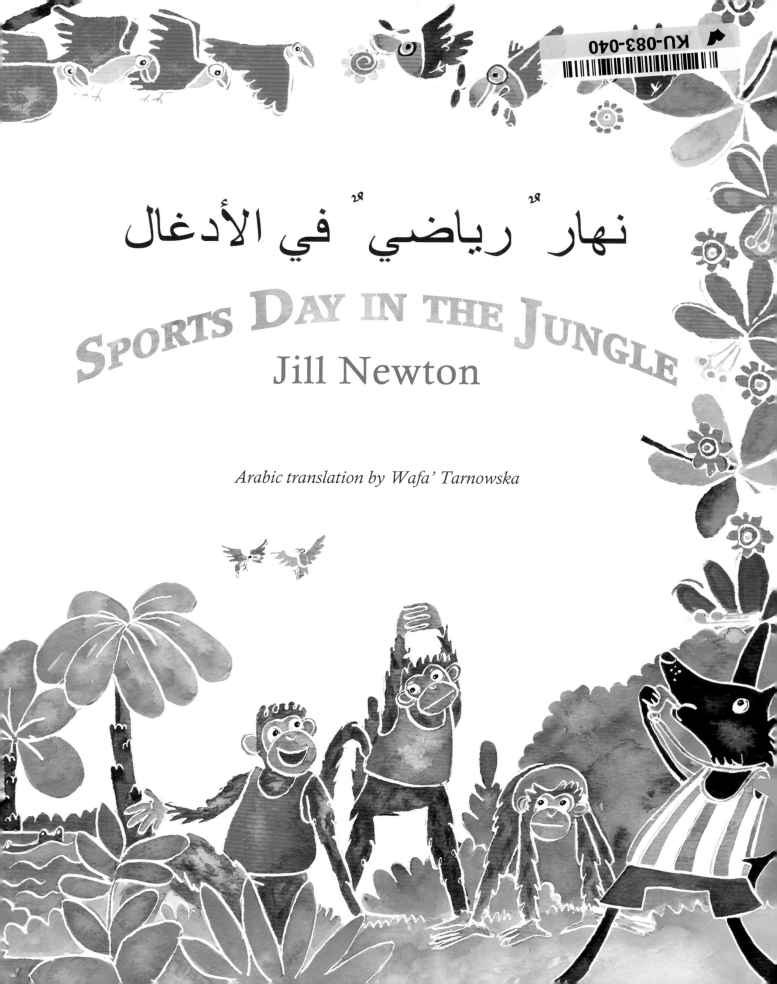

نهارٌ رياضيٌّ في الأدغال

SPORTS DAY IN THE JUNGLE

Jill Newton

Arabic translation by Wafa' Tarnowska

حانَ وقتُ العاب الأدغالِ ، فكانَ كلُ حيوانٍ
مشغول يتمرن.
بالفعل، نعني معظمُ الحيواناتِ وليسَ كلهم.

It was nearly time for the
jungle games, and every
animal was busy practising.

Well, *almost* every animal.

For Team McCallum:
Ben, Toby, Ella and Charlie.

Text copyright © 2010 Jill Newton
Illustrations copyright © 2010 Jill Newton
Dual language text copyright © 2010 Mantra Lingua
Audio copyright © 2010 Mantra Lingua
This edition 2010

Mantra Lingua
Global House
303 Ballards Lane
London, N12 8NP
www.mantralingua.com

Touch the arrow with the RecorderPEN to start

Start Info English Language

كانَ الحيوانُ الكسولُ يراقبُ بهدوءٍ من غصنِ الشجرةِ، لم يكنْ يتحركُ كثيراً .

Sloth slowly watched from his branch. He didn't move very much.

مرَ القردُ أمامه.
"أنظرْ إليَّ أيها الحيوانُ الكسول! حاولْ أن تقبضَ عليَّ!"

Monkey swung past.
"Look at me, Sloth! Try and catch me!"

رأى الحيوانُ الكسولُ القردَ يختفي
بين الأشجارِ ...
... فتنهد.

Sloth watched Monkey disappear
into the trees…

…and sighed.

رأى قرودَ الليمور تقفزُ،
والنمورَ تثبُ وقرودَ
الاورانغْ اوتانغ تتلاعبُ
في الأدغال.

He watched lemurs leap,
panthers pounce
and orangutans do the jungle juggle.

فاغمضَ الحيوانُ الكسولُ...

ببطءٍ ...

ببطءٍ عيناه ...

And Sloth slowly...
slowly...
slowly closed his eyes.

"You can't catch me, Sloth!"
Monkey laughed.

"لا تستطيعَ أن تقبضَ عليَ
أيها الحيوانُ الكسول!"
ضحكَ القرد .

رأى الحيوانُ الكسولُ القردَ يتأرجحُ بين الأغصانِ،
متوجها نحو فريقِ الاختيارِ .. فتنهد .

Sloth watched Monkey spin about on the
branches, swinging off to the team selections…

…and sighed.

كانَ ابنُ آوى يراقبُ كيف كانَ كلُ حيوانٍ
يعملُ كلَ ما في وسعه.
فاختارَ القردَ أولاً لأنَ القردَ كانَ يفوزُ دائماً.

Jackal looked on as every creature tried their best.
She chose Monkey first as Monkey *always* won.

لم ينتقِ أحدٌ الحيوانَ الكسول إذ لم
يكنْ هناك سباقٌ في التلوك.

Nobody chose Sloth.
There was no race for
hanging about.

كانَ فريقُ الحيوانات يعملُ باجتهاد. كانوا جميعاً يريدون حقًا الفوزَ بمباريات الأدغال.

The team worked hard. They all really wanted to win the jungle games.

"إنني سأفوزْ!" صاحَ القرد. "لا يستطيعُ أحد
أن يقبضَ عليّ!"
نظرتْ جميعُ الحيواناتِ إلى القردِ ... فتنهدت.

"I'm going to win!" called Monkey.
"No one can catch me!"
All the animals watched Monkey… and sighed.

بعدَ ليلٍ طويلٍ قلق أشرقتِ الشمسُ أخيراً.
ومعها جاءتْ فرقُ الحيواناتِ المتباريةِ.
كانتْ الأدغالُ **ناشطة** بالرياضةِ .

After a long, restless night the sun
finally appeared. And along with it
came the competing teams.

The jungle was alive with sport.

Slowly, Sloth moved branch to watch the tigers tumble, the toucans tango, the elephants humph and the frogs hop, skip and jump!

ببطءٍ، انتقلَ الحيوانُ الكسولُ إلى غصنٍ أقربٍ
لمشاهدة النمورِ تتشقلبُ، وطيورِ الطوقان ترقصُ
التانغو، والفيلة تهدرِ والضفادعِ تقفزُ
تثبُ، وتنط.

بعدَ حين ، لم يبقَ إلا سباقٌ واحد.

"سيكونُ السباقُ سهلاً" قال القردُ وهو يستعدُ له.

"انني سريعٌ مثل الريح. لا يستطيعُ أحدٌ،/عني لا

أحدٌ ، أن يقبضَ عليَّ!"

Soon there was only one race left.
"It'll be a breeze," said Monkey as he got ready.
"I'm as fast as the wind. No one, *I mean no one*,
can catch me!"

تسابقَ القردُ من غصنٍ إلى غصنٍ إلى كرمةٍ متأرجحاً
أسرع وأسرع .
هتفَ الجميعُ عندما أصبحتِ المسافةُ
بينه وبينَ الآخرين أوسع.

Monkey raced from bough to branch to vine,
swinging faster and faster.
Everyone cheered as the gap got wider.

قفزَ القردُ وأمسكَ بأعلى غصنٍ
في الشجرة ...

Monkey leapt and grabbed the
highest branch of the tree…

انكسرَ!

SNAP!

The branch
wasn't strong
enough.

لم يكنْ الغصنُ
قوياً جداً.

وقفَ الحيوانُ الكسولُ ببطءٍ ...
ببطءٍ ... على الغصن.

Sloth slowly…
slowly…
stood up on his branch.

مدَ ذراعيهِ الطويلين،
ثمَ ...
ووشْ!

He stretched his long arms,
then…

WHOOSH!

هتفَ الجميعُ عندما أنقذَ الحيوانُ
الكسولُ القردَ من السقوط.

Everyone cheered as
Sloth *finally* caught
Monkey!

JUNGLE FACTS

Sloths are surprisingly good at swimming

Lemurs use their big tails to signal to each other

Panthers are really good at climbing trees

When a male and female toucan like each other they use their beaks to throw fruit to each other

Elephants make lots of interesting noises. They grunt, purr, bellow, whistle and trumpet

Monkeys live in groups called troops

A tiger's roar can be heard more than a mile away

If people don't stop chopping down the jungle, very soon there won't be any jungle left